The Best of... Jethro

CW00666127

Wise Publications
London / New York / Paris / Sydney / Copenhagen / Madrid / Tokyo

Exclusive distributors:
Music Sales Limited
8/9 Frith Street,
London W1V 5TZ, England.
Music Sales Pty Limited
120 Rothschild Avenue
Rosebery, NSW 2018,
Australia.

Order No. AM966350
ISBN 0-7119-8392-5
This book © Copyright 2000 by Wise Publications

Cover design by Michael Bell Design

Cover photographs courtesy of Retna and London Features International
Compiled by Peter Evans

Printed in the United Kingdom by
Printwise (Haverhill) Limited, Haverhill, Suffolk.

Your Guarantee of Quality
As publishers, we strive to produce every book to
the highest commercial standards. The book has been carefully designed to
minimise awkward page turns and to make playing from it a real pleasure.
Particular care has been given to specifying acid-free, neutral-sized paper
made from pulps which have not been elemental chlorine bleached.
This pulp is from farmed sustainable forests and was produced
with special regard for the environment. Throughout, the printing and
binding have been planned to ensure a sturdy, attractive publication
which should give years of enjoyment. If your copy fails to meet
our high standards, please inform us and we will gladly replace it.

Music Sales' complete catalogue describes thousands of titles and is
available in full colour sections by subject, direct from Music Sales Limited.
Please state your areas of interest and send a cheque/postal order
for £1.50 for postage to: Music Sales Limited, Newmarket Road,
Bury St. Edmunds, Suffolk IP33 3YB.

www.musicsales.com

A NEW DAY YESTERDAY

Words & Music by Ian Anderson

And then I kissed you once. ___

___ to ___ turn out this way.

Oh, _____ I want to see ___

I _____ ___ had ___ to ___

___ you soon, _____ but I won - der how. ___

leave to - day _____ ___ just when ___ I ___

It was A NEW DAY ___ YES-TER-DAY ___

thought I'd found ___ you; It was A NEW DAY ___ YES-TER-DAY ___

To Coda ⊕

4

AQUALUNG

Words & Music by Ian Anderson & Jennie Anderson

snot is run-ning down his nose,

greas - y fin-gers smear-ing shab - by clothes._____

Hey, Aq - ua - lung.   Dry-ing in the cold sun,

watch-ing as the fril - ly pant - ies run.

old man wan-d'ring lone-ly, taking time the
ar-my's up the road,— sal-va-tion à la

on-ly way— he knows. Legs— hurt-ing
mode and a cup of tea. Aq-ua-lung, my

bad— as he bends to pick a dog-end. He
friend,— don't you start a-way un-eas-y. You

goes down to the bog— and warms his feet.
poor old sod, you see— it's on-ly me.

sounds and the flow-ers bloom like mad - ness in the

spring.

Oh,_____ Aq - ua - lung.

11

LIVING IN THE PAST

Words & Music by Ian Anderson

Hap - py__ and I'm
Once I__ used to

smil - ing,__ walk a mile to__ drink your wa - ter.__ You
join in__ ev - 'ry boy and__ girl was my friend.__

know I'd _____ love to love you _____ and a - bove you _____ there's no
Now there's _____ rev - o - lu - tion, _____ but they don't know _____ what they're

oth - er. _____ We'll go _____ walk - ing out _____ while oth - ers
fight - ing. _____ Let us _____ close our eyes; _____ out - side their

shout _____ of war's dis - as - ter. Oh, _____ we won't
lives _____ go on much fast - er. Oh, _____ we won't

give in, _____ let's go liv - ing _____ in the past. _____
give in, _____ we'll keep liv - ing _____ in the

LOCOMOTIVE BREATH

Words & Music by Ian Anderson

16

death. Oh,— he feels the pis - ton scrap - ing, steam break-ing on his
fun. Oh,—he's crawl-ing down— the cor - ri -dor on his hands and
balls. Oh,— he picks up Gid - e-on's Bi - ble, o - pen at page

brow.—   Old Char-lie stole— the han - dle,
knees.—   Old Char-lie stole— the han - dle, } and the train, it won't stop
one.—   I thank God he stole— the han -dle,

go-ing, no way to slow down.—   Oh,   oh.—

1. 2.

No way to slow down.—   No way to slow

3.

Repeat and fade

NOTHING IS EASY

Words & Music by Ian Anderson

ten-sion starts mount-ing and you've lost count of the pen-nies you've
if you're a-lone and you're down to the bone, just give us a

missed,
play.
just try hard and see why they're
You'll smile in a while and dis-

not wor-ry'ng me,___ they're last on my list.
cov-er that I'll get you hap-py my way.

N.C.

Noth-ing's eas-y.
Noth-ing's eas-y.

SONGS FROM THE WOOD

WORDS & MUSIC BY IAN ANDERSON

Moderately Fast

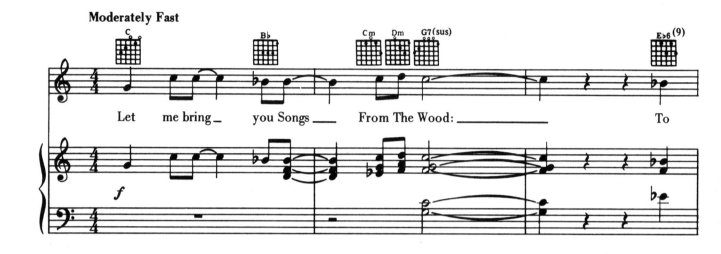

Let me bring you Songs From The Wood: To

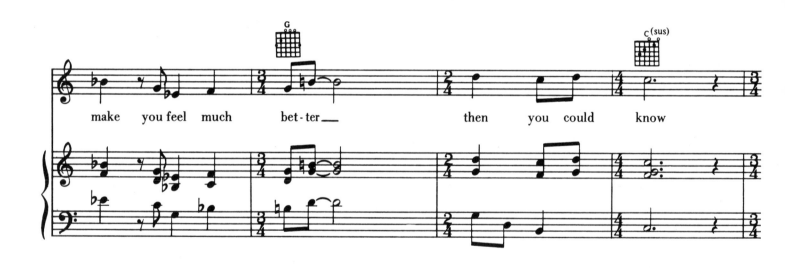

make you feel much bet-ter then you could know

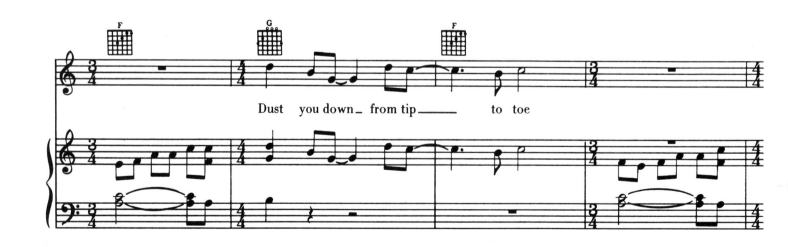

Dust you down from tip to toe

Show you how__ the gar - den grows__

Hold you stead - y as __ you go__

Join __ the chor - us if __ you can: It - 'll make of you an hon -

- est man. __

As you drag down ev - ery lov - ers' lane.

Life's long cel - e - bra - tion's

here. I'll toast you all __ in __

__ pen - ny cheer. _____

24

I am the cross to take____ your nail:

A sing - er of ___ these age - less times ___

With kitch - en prose and ___

gut - ter rhymes. _____

STEEL MONKEY

Words & Music by Ian Anderson

Feel___ me climb-ing up your knee.___
keep me from fall-ing
we bolt those dreams, then

Guess what I am.___ I'm a steel mon-key.___

SWEET DREAM

Words & Music by Ian Anderson

Moderately, with a beat

You'll hear me call-ing in your sweet dream,
No one can see us in your sweet dream,

can't hear your dad-dy's warn-ing cry.
don't hear you leave to start the car.

TEACHER

WORDS & MUSIC BY IAN ANDERSON

had a les - son that I must im - part to you. It's an old ex - pres - sion but I must in - sist it's true. Jump up, look a - round, find your-self some fun, no sense in sit-ting there hat - ing ev - 'ry-one.

38

No man's an is-land and his cas-tle is-n't home, __ the nest is full of noth-ing when __ the bird __ has flown. __

So, I

39

took   a jour-ney, ___   threw my world in - to the   sea. _____   With me ___
teach - er told me ___   it had been a   lot of   fun. _____   Thanked me ___

___ went the teach - er   who found fun in-stead of me. _____
___ for his tick - et   and ___ all that I   had done. _____

Hey, man, what's the plan, ___ what was that you   said? _____   Sun - tanned, drink in hand, ly-

- ing there in bed. _____   I try to so-cial-ize ___ but I ___ can't seem to   find _____

what I was look-ing for,— got some-thing on — my mind.————

Then the

TOO OLD TO ROCK 'N' ROLL, TOO YOUNG TO DIE

Words & Music by Ian Anderson

1. The old____ rock-er wore his hair too long,____
2. He once owned a Har-ley Dav-id-son,____
3. 3rd Verse

____ wore his trou-ser cuffs too tight.____ Un-fash-ion-a-ble
____ and a Tri-umph Bon-ne-ville,____ count-ed his friends____ in

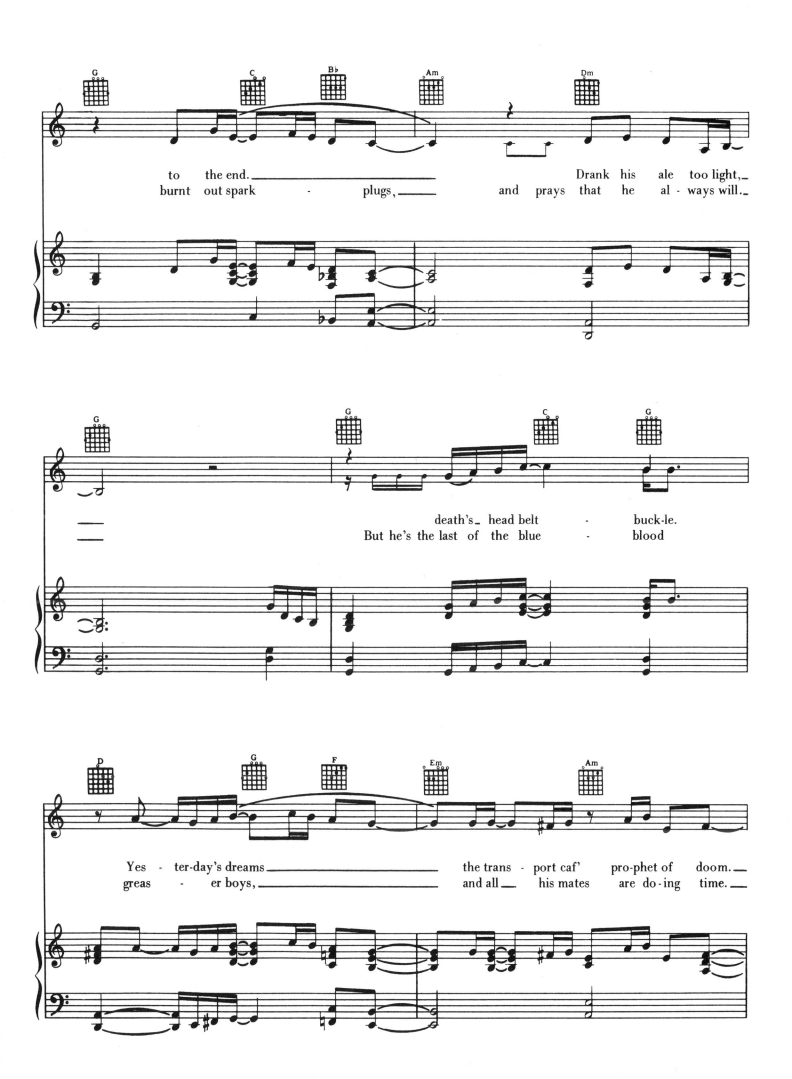

44

3rd VERSE

So the old rocker gets out his bike,
    to make a ton before he takes his leave
    upon the al by Scotch Corner just like it used to be.
And as he flies, tears in his eyes,
    his wind-whipped words echo the final take,
    as he hits the trunk road doing around one-hundred twenty
    with no room left to brake.   *(Chorus)*
And he was Too Old To Rock N' Roll,
    and he was Too Young To Die.
Yes he was Too Old To Rock N' Roll,
    but he was Too Young To Die.

01/07 (60732)